SCHOLASTIC

Do The Math™

Created by
Marilyn Burns

 **Division** Ⓐ

Basic Concepts

....

WorkSpace

Copyright © 2008 by Scholastic Inc.

All rights reserved.   Published by Scholastic Inc.   Printed in the U.S.A.

ISBN-13: 978-0-545-01353-6
ISBN-10: 0-545-01353-4

SCHOLASTIC, DO THE MATH, and associated logos and designs are trademarks and/or registered trademarks of Scholastic Inc.

1 2 3 4 5 6 7 8 9 10   40   16 15 14 13 12 11 10 09 08 07

Sharing 12 Cookies

DIRECTIONS

1 3 children share 12 cookies.

Draw a picture to show sharing 12 cookies among the number of children.

2

$$12 \div 3 = 4 \qquad \frac{12}{3} = 4$$

$$3)\overline{12}^{\,4}$$

Write the division in three ways.

---

① 2 children share 12 cookies.

② 4 children share 12 cookies.

③ 6 children share 12 cookies.

④ 12 children share 12 cookies.

Lesson 2

Home Note: Your child models sharing situations and represents them with numbers and symbols.

More Ways to Share 12 Cookies

➤ Draw a picture to show sharing 12 cookies among the number of children.

➤ Write the division in three ways.

① 1 child shares 12 cookies.

② 3 children share 12 cookies.

Home Note: Your child continues to model sharing situations and represent them with numbers and symbols.

More Ways to Share 12 Cookies

➤ Draw a picture to show sharing 12 cookies among the number of children.

➤ Write the division in three ways.

(1) 9 children share 12 cookies.

(2) 11 children share 12 cookies.

Lesson 4

Home Note: Your child encounters remainders while modeling more sharing situations.

Show What You Know

➤ Draw a picture to show sharing 12 cookies among the number of children.

➤ Write the division in three ways.

---

1 4 children share 12 cookies.

2 10 children share 12 cookies.

Home Note: Your child describes sharing situations by drawing and writing three representations using numbers and symbols.

More Ways to Share 12 Cookies

➤ Draw a picture to show sharing 12 cookies among the number of children.

➤ Write the division in three ways.

---

1 8 children share 12 cookies.

2 9 children share 12 cookies.

Lesson 5

 Home Note: Your child describes sharing situations by drawing and writing three representations using numbers and symbols.

Packaging 12 Pencils

DIRECTIONS

1 **12 pencils in packages of 3**

☐☐☐ ☐☐☐

☐☐☐ ☐☐☐

Draw a picture showing how you grouped 12 pencils into the packages.

2

$12 \div 3 = 4$ $\frac{12}{3} = 4$

$3\overline{)12}$ with quotient 4

Write the division in three ways.

---

① 12 pencils in packages of 2

② 12 pencils in packages of 4

③ 12 pencils in packages of 6

Home Note: Your child describes grouping situations in drawings and represents division with numbers and symbols.

Lesson 6

7

Packaging 12 Pencils

➤ Draw a picture showing how you grouped 12 pencils into the packages.

➤ Write the division in three ways.

(1) 12 pencils in packages of 1

(2) 12 pencils in packages of 7

(3) 12 pencils in packages of 5

Lesson 7

Home Note: Your child solves and represents grouping division problems, some of which have remainders.

Packaging 12 Pencils

DIRECTIONS

➤ Draw a picture showing how you grouped 12 pencils into the packages.

➤ Write the division in three ways.

---

① 12 pencils in packages of 9

---

② 12 pencils in packages of 3

---

③ 12 pencils in packages of 11

Home Note: Your child continues to solve and represent
grouping division problems with remainders.

Packaging 10 Pencils

DIRECTIONS

➤ Draw a picture showing how you grouped 10 pencils into the packages.

➤ Write the division in three ways.

① 10 pencils in packages of 2

② 10 pencils in packages of 1

③ 10 pencils in packages of 3

Lesson 8

Home Note: Your child solves and represents grouping division problems with and without remainders.

Packaging 10 Pencils

DIRECTIONS

➤ Draw a picture showing how you grouped 10 pencils into the packages.

➤ Write the division in three ways.

---

(1) 10 pencils in packages of 4

---

(2) 10 pencils in packages of 5

---

(3) 10 pencils in packages of 6

Home Note: Your child continues to solve and represent
grouping division problems with and without remainders.

Packaging 10 Pencils

DIRECTIONS

➤ Draw a picture showing how you grouped 10 pencils into the packages.

➤ Write the division in three ways.

① 10 pencils in packages of 7

② 10 pencils in packages of 8

Lesson 8

Home Note: Your child continues to solve and represent grouping division problems with and without remainders.

Packaging 10 Pencils

DIRECTIONS

➤ Draw a picture showing how you grouped 10 pencils into the packages.

➤ Write the division in three ways.

① 10 pencils in packages of 9

② 10 pencils in packages of 10

Home Note: Your child continues to solve and represent grouping division problems with and without remainders.

Model Two Kinds of Problems for 8 ÷ 4

DIRECTIONS

1

6 ÷ 2
sharing

☐☐☐   ☐☐☐

Model the problem with tiles.
Draw a picture.

2

6 ÷ 2 = 3

$\frac{6}{2} = 3$ $2\overline{)6}^{\,3}$

Write the division
in three ways.

3

6 tiles divided
between 2 children
gives each child
3 tiles.

Write the problem in words.

1

SHARING

Draw a picture.	Write the division in three ways.	Write the problem in words.

2

GROUPING

Draw a picture.	Write the division in three ways.	Write the problem in words.

 Home Note: Your child compares sharing problems and grouping problems by writing, modeling, and representing an example of each.

Model Two Kinds of Problems for 13 ÷ 3

1

6 ÷ 2
sharing

☐☐☐ ☐☐☐

Model the problem with tiles.
Draw a picture.

2

6 ÷ 2 = 3

$\frac{6}{2} = 3$ $2\overline{)6}^{\,3}$

Write the division
in three ways.

3

6 tiles divided
between 2 children
gives each child
3 tiles.

Write the problem in words.

① SHARING

Draw a picture.	Write the division in three ways.	Write the problem in words.

② GROUPING

Draw a picture.	Write the division in three ways.	Write the problem in words.

Home Note: Your child compares sharing problems and grouping problems
by writing, modeling, and representing an example of each.

Lesson 9

15

Show What You Know

DIRECTIONS

➤ Draw a picture showing the problem 14 ÷ 4.

➤ Write the division in three ways.

➤ Write the problem in words.

1 | **SHARING 14 ÷ 4**

Draw a picture.	Write the division in three ways.	Write the problem in words.

2 | **GROUPING 14 ÷ 4**

Draw a picture.	Write the division in three ways.	Write the problem in words.

Home Note: Your child models, solves, and compares sharing and grouping division problems.

Model Two Kinds of Problems for ☐ ÷ 3

DIRECTIONS

➤ Grab a handful of tiles and count them.

➤ Use the number as the missing number in the problem ☐ ÷ 3.

➤ Draw a picture showing the problem.

➤ Write the division in three ways.

➤ Write the problem in words.

① SHARING

Draw a picture.	Write the division in three ways.	Write the problem in words.

② GROUPING

Draw a picture.	Write the division in three ways.	Write the problem in words.

Home Note: Your child models, solves, and compares sharing and grouping division problems.

Exchanging a Handful of Pennies for Dimes

1

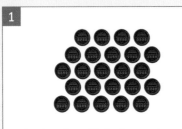

Grab a handful of pennies.

2

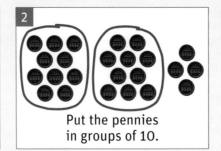

Put the pennies
in groups of 10.

3

The number of pennies
in my handful is __24__.

Answer the questions.

① The number of pennies in my handful is _____.

② Draw how you grouped the pennies. Circle the groups of 10.

③ Fill in the blanks: _____ pennies equals _____ groups of _____ with _____ left over.

④ Write the division in three ways.

⑤ My pennies are worth _____ dimes.

🏠 **Home Note:** Your child practices dividing by 10, exchanging
dimes for pennies, and writing equations to show the division.

How Many Dimes? How Many Pennies Left Over?

DIRECTIONS

1 15 pennies	2	3	4
 Put the pennies in groups of 10.	1 Write the number of dimes you would get for the pennies.	5 Write the number of pennies left over.	$15 \div 10 = 1 \text{ R}5$ Write an equation for the division.

	Number of dimes you could get	Number of pennies left over	Equation
32 pennies			
46 pennies			
25 pennies			
13 pennies			
58 pennies			

Home Note: Your child looks for patterns in quotients and remainders when dividing by 10.

Exchanging a Handful of Dimes for Dollars

➤ You and your partner each grab a handful of dimes.

➤ Answer the questions for your handful of dimes, and for your partner's.

(1) The number of dimes in my handful is _____.

(2) Draw how you grouped your dimes. Circle the groups of 10.

(3) I can trade my dimes for _____ dollars with _____ dimes left over.

(4) Write an equation for the division.

(5) The number of dimes in my partner's handful is _____.

(6) Draw how you grouped your partner's dimes. Circle the groups of 10.

(7) My partner can trade the dimes for _____ dollars with _____ dimes left over.

(8) Write an equation for the division.

Home Note: Your child practices dividing by 10, exchanging dimes for dollars, and then representing the division numerically.

How Many Dollars? How Many Dimes Left Over?

DIRECTIONS

1 15 dimes

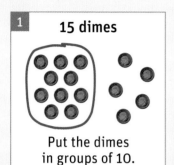

Put the dimes in groups of 10.

2 1

Write the number of dollars you would get for the dimes.

3 5

Write the number of dimes left over.

4 $15 \div 10 = 1\ R5$

Write an equation for the division.

	Number of dollars you could get	Number of dimes left over	Equation
25 dimes			
34 dimes			
17 dimes			
21 dimes			
53 dimes			
49 dimes			

Home Note: Your child continues to practice finding patterns in quotients and remainders when dividing by 10.

Show What You Know

➤ Read the problem.

➤ Answer the questions and ring the groups of coins.

(1) **You have 95 pennies that you want to exchange for dimes.**

Show how to group the pennies.

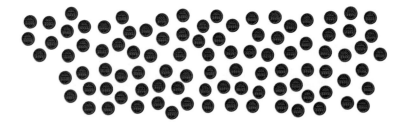

The number of dimes you can get is _____.

The number of leftover pennies you will have is _____.

The division equation is _____.

(2) **You have 56 dimes that you want to exchange for dollars.**

Show how to group the dimes.

The number of dollars you can get is _____.

The number of leftover dimes you will have is _____.

The division equation is _____.

Home Note: Your child models, solves, and writes an equation for grouping division problems with and without remainders.

Handfuls of Dimes

DIRECTIONS

➤ You and your partner each grab a handful of dimes.

➤ Work together to answer the questions.

---

(1) My number of dimes is _____.

My partner's number of dimes is _____.

Together we have _____ dimes.

We can get _____ dollars with _____ dimes left over.

Our equation is _____.

➤ You and your partner each grab another handful of dimes.

➤ Work together to answer the questions for the new handfuls of dimes.

---

(2) My number of dimes is _____.

My partner's number of dimes is _____.

Together we have _____ dimes.

We can get _____ dollars with _____ dimes left over.

Our equation is _____.

Home Note: Your child solves and writes equations for grouping division problems with and without remainders.

Game Rules for Leftovers

What you need

- number cube (1–6)
- 15 tiles
- cup to hold the tiles
- 6 sheets of paper
- *WorkSpace* page 25 or 26
- pencil

➤ **Players take turns. Each turn has three steps.**

1

Roll the number cube, and set out the
number of sheets of paper shown on the cube.

2

Share the tiles from the cup equally on
the sheets of paper. Keep the leftovers.

3

$$15 \div 4 = 3\,R3$$

Return the tiles on the sheets of paper to the cup.
Both players record the equation.

➤ **Play continues until there are no tiles.**

➤ **The player with the greatest number of leftovers wins.**

Home Note: Your child learns the rules to a game in
which he or she practices solving sharing problems.

Leftovers—Practice Game

DIRECTIONS

1 Roll the number cube, and set out the number of sheets of paper shown on the cube.

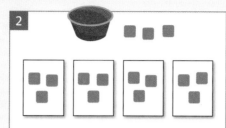

2 Share the tiles from the cup equally on the sheets of paper. Keep the leftovers.

3 $15 \div 4 = 3\,R3$

Return the tiles on the sheets of paper to the cup.
Both players record the equation.

Player A	Player B

Total leftovers: _____

Total leftovers: _____

Home Note: Your child practices solving sharing problems and writing equations by playing a game.

Leftovers

1 Roll the number cube, and set out the number of sheets of paper shown on the cube.

2 Share the tiles from the cup equally on the sheets of paper. Keep the leftovers.

3 $15 \div 4 = 3\,R3$

Return the tiles on the sheets of paper to the cup. Both players record the equation.

Player A	Player B

Total leftovers: _____   Total leftovers: _____

26   Lesson 17   **Home Note:** Your child records the division from the game *Leftovers*.

Leftovers

DIRECTIONS

1 Roll the number cube, and set out the number of sheets of paper shown on the cube.

2 Share the tiles from the cup equally on the sheets of paper. Keep the leftovers.

3 $15 \div 4 = 3\,R3$

Return the tiles on the sheets of paper to the cup. Both players record the equation.

Player A	Player B

Total leftovers: _____   **Total leftovers:** _____

Home Note: Your child records the division from the game *Leftovers*.

Leftovers

1 Roll the number cube, and set out the number of sheets of paper shown on the cube.

2 Share the tiles from the cup equally on the sheets of paper. Keep the leftovers.

3 $15 \div 4 = 3\,R3$

Return the tiles on the sheets of paper to the cup. Both players record the equation.

Player A	Player B

Total leftovers: _____   Total leftovers: _____

Home Note: Your child records the division from the game *Leftovers.*

Leftovers

DIRECTIONS

1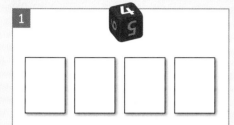

Roll the number cube, and set out the number of sheets of paper shown on the cube.

2

Share the tiles from the cup equally on the sheets of paper. Keep the leftovers.

3

$15 \div 4 = 3\,R3$

Return the tiles on the sheets of paper to the cup.
Both players record the equation.

Player A	Player B

Total leftovers: _____   Total leftovers: _____

Home Note: Your child records the division from a variation of the game *Leftovers*.

Leftovers

DIRECTIONS

1

Roll the number cube, and set out the number of sheets of paper shown on the cube.

2

Share the tiles from the cup equally on the sheets of paper. Keep the leftovers.

3

$15 \div 4 = 3\,R3$

Return the tiles on the sheets of paper to the cup.
Both players record the equation.

Player A	Player B

Total leftovers: _____

Total leftovers: _____

Home Note: Your child practices solving sharing problems when playing a variation of the game *Leftovers*.

Show What You Know

➤ Complete the division equations. You may use tiles to figure out the quotients and remainders.

① $20 \div 6 =$ _____	② $12 \div 5 =$ _____
③ $24 \div 4 =$ _____	④ $8 \div 3 =$ _____
⑤ $18 \div 3 =$ _____	⑥ $17 \div 4 =$ _____
⑦ $20 \div 3 =$ _____	⑧ $11 \div 2 =$ _____
⑨ $13 \div 5 =$ _____	⑩ $14 \div 7 =$ _____
⑪ $19 \div 4 =$ _____	⑫ $10 \div 6 =$ _____

Home Note: Your child completes equations for a two-digit number divided by a one-digit number.

Leftovers

DIRECTIONS

1 Roll the number cube, and set out the number of sheets of paper shown on the cube.

2 Share the tiles from the cup equally on the sheets of paper. Keep the leftovers.

3 $15 \div 4 = 3\,R3$

Return the tiles on the sheets of paper to the cup. Both players record the equation.

Player A	Player B

Total leftovers: _____   Total leftovers: _____

Home Note: Your child practices solving sharing problems and writing equations by playing the game *Leftovers*.

Division Problems Using 3, 4, and 2

➤ Copy the first two division problems from the board.

➤ Write the other four division problems that can be made using 3, 4, and 2.

➤ When your teacher tells you, model each division with tiles and draw it in the box.

➤ Write the quotient and remainder for each problem.

① 34	② 32
③ 43	④ 42
⑤ 23	⑥ 24

Home Note: Your child writes and solves division problems by rearranging three numbers to make six division problems.

Steps for Writing Division Problems

1

Roll 3 number cubes.

2

If any numbers are the same, roll one cube again
until all three numbers are different.

3

24 ÷ 5	45 ÷ 2	52 ÷ 4
25 ÷ 4	42 ÷ 5	54 ÷ 2

Use all three numbers for your division problems.

Home Note: Your child refers to these rules for creating
division problems from the rolls of three number cubes.

Division Problems with 1, 5, and 3

➤ Write six division problems using the numbers 1, 5, and 3.

---

(1) Problems

_____   _____

_____   _____

_____   _____

➤ Write a division equation for each problem.

---

(2) Equations

_____   _____

_____   _____

_____   _____

Home Note: Your child practices writing and solving all of the possible division problems using three numbers.

Game Rules for Remainder Zero

What you need

- 3 number cubes (1, 2, 2, 3, 4, 5)
- tiles
- 5 sheets of paper
- *WorkSpace* page 37 or 38
- pencil

➤ **Each pair plays against another pair.**

➤ **Each turn has four steps.**

1

Roll the three number cubes, and
record the numbers that you roll.

2

34 ÷ 2	43 ÷ 2
32 ÷ 4	23 ÷ 4
42 ÷ 3	24 ÷ 3

Write 6 division problems using
the numbers you rolled.

3

34 ÷ 2 = 17 R0	43 ÷ 2 = 21 R1
32 ÷ 4 = 8 R0	23 ÷ 4 = 5 R3
42 ÷ 3 = 14 R0	24 ÷ 3 = 8 R0

Use tiles to solve the problems, and
write an equation for each one.

4

The number of zero remainders is $\boxed{4}$.

Write the total number of zero remainders.

➤ **The pair with the greater number of zero remainders wins.**

 Home Note: Your child learns the rules for playing a division game.

Remainder Zero—Practice Turn

➤ Write six division problems using the numbers shown on the number cubes.

➤ Write a division equation for each problem.

➤ Record the number of zero remainders.

Problems

_____   _____

_____   _____

_____   _____

Equations

_____   _____

_____   _____

_____   _____

The number of zero remainders is ⬚ .

Home Note: Your child practices writing and solving division equations by playing a game.

Remainder Zero

DIRECTIONS

1

$34 \div 2$ $43 \div 2$

$32 \div 4$ $23 \div 4$

$42 \div 3$ $24 \div 3$

Write 6 division problems using the numbers you rolled.

2

$34 \div 2 = 17\,R0$ $43 \div 2 = 21\,R1$

$32 \div 4 = 8\,R0$ $23 \div 4 = 5\,R3$

$42 \div 3 = 14\,R0$ $24 \div 3 = 8\,R0$

Use tiles to solve the problems, and write an equation for each one.

3

The number of zero remainders is $\boxed{4}$.

Write the total number of zero remainders.

Numbers Rolled

Problems

_____   _____

_____   _____

_____   _____

Equations

_____   _____

_____   _____

_____   _____

The number of zero remainders is $\boxed{}$.

 Home Note: Your child practices writing and solving division equations by playing a game.

Remainder One

1

34 ÷ 2   43 ÷ 2
32 ÷ 4   23 ÷ 4
42 ÷ 3   24 ÷ 3

Write 6 division problems
using the numbers you rolled.

2

34 ÷ 2 = 17 R0   43 ÷ 2 = 21 R1
32 ÷ 4 = 8 R0   23 ÷ 4 = 5 R3
42 ÷ 3 = 14 R0   24 ÷ 3 = 8 R0

Use tiles to solve the problems,
and write an equation for each one.

3

The number of

remainders of 1 is [1].

Record the number
of remainders of 1.

Numbers Rolled

Problems

_____   _____

_____   _____

_____   _____

Equations

_____   _____

_____   _____

_____   _____

The number of remainders of 1 is [   ].

Home Note: Your child practices writing and solving division equations by playing a game.

Lesson 24   39

Remainder One

DIRECTIONS

1

34 ÷ 2   43 ÷ 2

32 ÷ 4   23 ÷ 4

42 ÷ 3   24 ÷ 3

Write 6 division problems
using the numbers you rolled.

2

34 ÷ 2 = 17 R0   43 ÷ 2 = 21 R1

32 ÷ 4 = 8 R0   23 ÷ 4 = 5 R3

42 ÷ 3 = 14 R0   24 ÷ 3 = 8 R0

Use tiles to solve the problems,
and write an equation for each one.

3

The number of

remainders of 1 is ⟨1⟩.

Record the number
of remainders of 1.

Numbers Rolled

Problems

_____   _____

_____   _____

_____   _____

Equations

_____   _____

_____   _____

_____   _____

The number of remainders of 1 is ⟨ ⟩.

Home Note: Your child practices writing and solving division equations by playing a game.

Show What You Know

DIRECTIONS

➤ Complete the Remainder Zero game.

Numbers Rolled

2   5   4

Problems

$25 \div 4$	54
$24 \div 5$	
52	

Equations

$25 \div 4 = 6 \text{ R}1$	54
$24 \div 5 =$	
52	

The number of zero remainders is ☐.

Home Note: Your child writes and solves all of the possible division problems using three given numbers.

Leftovers

DIRECTIONS

1 Roll the number cube, and set out the number of sheets of paper shown on the cube.

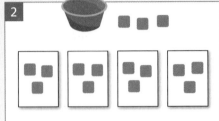

2 Share the tiles from the cup equally on the sheets of paper. Keep the leftovers.

3

$15 \div 4 = 3\,R3$

Return the tiles on the sheets of paper to the cup. Both players record the equation.

Player A	Player B

Total leftovers: _____   Total leftovers: _____

Lesson 25

Home Note: Your child practices solving sharing problems and writing equations by playing a game.

Word Problems for 32 ÷ 4

EXAMPLES

Grouping Problem	**Sharing Problem**
There are 32 ___patches___ .	There are 32 ___balloons___ .
There will be 4 on each ___jacket___ .	They will be shared among ___4 people___ .
How many ___jackets___ are there in all?	How many ___balloons___ will each get?

Here is a grouping problem and a sharing problem with blanks to help you when writing your own problem on page 44.

GROUPING

There are 32 _____.

There will be 4 in each _____.

How many _____ are there in all?

SHARING

There are 32 _____.

They will be shared among 4 _____.

How many _____ will each get?

Home Note: Your child uses sample problems to help write and solve his or her own sharing or grouping word problem.

Write a Word Problem for 32 ÷ 4

➤ Work with your partner to think of a word problem.

➤ Write the word problem.

➤ Solve the problem. Draw a picture and write the equation.

➤ Write whether the problem is a *sharing* or a *grouping* problem.

The word problem:

_____

_____

_____

_____

Draw a picture that shows how to solve the problem.

Division equation: _____

Is this a grouping or a sharing problem? _____

Home Note: Your child writes and solves a sharing or grouping word problem.

Write a Division Problem from List A

➤ Choose a division problem from List A. Do not write it on this page.

➤ Write a word problem for the division problem you chose.

The word problem:

_____

_____

_____

_____

_____

Home Note: Your child chooses a division problem,
and then writes a word problem for it.

Show How to Solve Your Problem

DIRECTIONS

➤ Draw a picture to show the word problem you wrote on page 45.

➤ Write the division in one of the three ways.

➤ Write the solution to the word problem.

The problem from List A is _____.

Draw a picture that shows how to solve the problem.

Write the division in one of the three ways. _____

The solution to my word problem:

_____

_____

Home Note: Your child shows how to solve the word problem from the previous page.

Write a Division Problem from List B

> ➤ Choose a division problem from List B. Do not write it on this page.
> ➤ Write a word problem for the division problem you chose.

The word problem:

_____

_____

_____

_____

Home Note: Your child chooses a division problem, and then writes a word problem for it.

Show How to Solve Your Problem

The problem from List B is _____.

Draw a picture that shows how to solve the problem.

Write the division in one of the three ways. _____

The solution to my word problem:

_____

_____

Lesson 27

Home Note: Your child shows how to solve the word problem from the previous page.

Write About Division

DIRECTIONS

➤ Tell about division with words, numbers, and pictures.

ABOUT DIVISION

Home Note: Your child reviews what he or she has learned about division.

Solve a Word Problem

> ➤ Draw a picture to show the problem.
> ➤ Write the division equation.
> ➤ Write the solution to the word problem.

The problem:

There are 28 stickers.
They will be shared equally among 7 people.
How many stickers will each person get?

Draw a picture that shows how to solve the problem.

Write the division equation. _____

The solution to the word problem:

_____

_____

Home Note: Your child solves a word problem.

Solve a Word Problem

➤ Draw a picture to show the problem.

➤ Write the division equation.

➤ Write the solution to the word problem.

The problem:

I have 33 stamps to put in an album.
Each page will have 6 stamps.
How many pages will I fill?

Draw a picture that shows how to solve the problem.

Write the division equation. _____

The solution to the word problem:

_____

_____

Home Note: Your child solves a word problem.

Leftovers

1 Roll the number cube, and set out the number of sheets of paper shown on the cube.

2 Share the tiles from the cup equally on the sheets of paper. Keep the leftovers.

3 $15 \div 4 = 3\,R3$

Return the tiles on the sheets of paper to the cup. Both players record the equation.

Player A	Player B

Total leftovers: _____   Total leftovers: _____

Home Note: Your child practices writing and solving division equations by playing a game.

Remainder Zero

DIRECTIONS

1

$34 \div 2$ $43 \div 2$

$32 \div 4$ $23 \div 4$

$42 \div 3$ $24 \div 3$

Write 6 division problems
using the numbers you rolled.

2

$34 \div 2 = 17 R0$ $43 \div 2 = 21 R1$

$32 \div 4 = 8 R0$ $23 \div 4 = 5 R3$

$42 \div 3 = 14 R0$ $24 \div 3 = 8 R0$

Use tiles to solve the problems,
and write an equation for each one.

3

The number of zero

remainders is $\boxed{4}$.

Write the total number
of zero remainders.

Numbers Rolled

Problems

_____   _____

_____   _____

_____   _____

Equations

_____   _____

_____   _____

_____   _____

The number of zero remainders is $\boxed{}$.

Home Note: Your child practices writing and solving division equations by playing a game.

Show What You Know

DIRECTIONS

➤ Complete each division equation.

① 24 ÷ 3 = _____

② 30 ÷ 9 = _____

③ 40 ÷ 6 = _____

④ 29 ÷ 7 = _____

⑤ 54 ÷ 9 = _____

⑥ 34 ÷ 8 = _____

Home Note: Your child solves division problems.

Show What You Know

DIRECTIONS

➤ Solve each word problem. Draw a picture and write an equation for each.

➤ Tell whether the problem is a grouping problem or a sharing problem.

---

1 Mona has 20 beads.
She uses 3 beads for each bracelet she is making.
How many bracelets can she make?

Draw a picture.

Division equation: _____

Is this a grouping or a sharing problem? _____

---

2 There are 32 baseball cards.
4 friends want to share them equally.
How many cards will each friend get?

Draw a picture.

Division equation: _____

Is this a grouping or a sharing problem? _____

Home Note: Your child solves division problems and
explains whether they are grouping or sharing problems.

Show What You Know

➤ Write a word problem for 40 ÷ 4.

➤ Draw a picture to show how to solve it.

➤ Write a division equation showing the problem.

➤ Tell if the problem is a grouping problem or a sharing problem.

The word problem:

_____

_____

_____

Draw a picture that shows how to solve the problem.

Division equation: _____

Is this a grouping or a sharing problem? _____

Home Note: Your child writes and solves a division problem and explains whether it is a grouping or sharing problem.

Leftovers

DIRECTIONS

1

Roll the number cube, and set out the number of sheets of paper shown on the cube.

2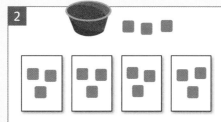

Share the tiles from the cup equally on the sheets of paper. Keep the leftovers.

3

$15 \div 4 = 3\,R3$

Return the tiles on the sheets of paper to the cup. Both players record the equation.

Player A	Player B

Total leftovers: _____

Total leftovers: _____

Home Note: Your child records the division from a variation of the game *Leftovers*.

Remainder Zero

DIRECTIONS

1

34 ÷ 2	43 ÷ 2
32 ÷ 4	23 ÷ 4
42 ÷ 3	24 ÷ 3

Write 6 division problems using the numbers you rolled.

2

34 ÷ 2 = 17 R0 43 ÷ 2 = 21 R1
32 ÷ 4 = 8 R0 23 ÷ 4 = 5 R3
42 ÷ 3 = 14 R0 24 ÷ 3 = 8 R0

Use tiles to solve the problems, and write an equation for each one.

3

The number of zero remainders is 4 .

Write the total number of zero remainders.

Numbers Rolled

Problems

_____   _____

_____   _____

_____   _____

Equations

_____   _____

_____   _____

_____   _____

The number of zero remainders is [ ] .

Home Note: Your child practices writing and solving division equations by playing a game.

Remainder One

1

34 ÷ 2	43 ÷ 2
32 ÷ 4	23 ÷ 4
42 ÷ 3	24 ÷ 3

Write 6 division problems using the numbers you rolled.

2

34 ÷ 2 = 17 R0	43 ÷ 2 = 21 R1
32 ÷ 4 = 8 R0	23 ÷ 4 = 5 R3
42 ÷ 3 = 14 R0	24 ÷ 3 = 8 R0

Use tiles to solve the problems, and write an equation for each one.

3

The number of remainders of 1 is ⬚ 1 ⬚.

Record the number of remainders of 1.

Numbers Rolled

Problems

_____ _____

_____ _____

_____ _____

Equations

_____ _____

_____ _____

_____ _____

The number of remainders of 1 is ⬚.

Home Note: Your child practices writing and solving division equations by playing a game.

Leftovers—for 3 Players

DIRECTIONS

➤ Record each player's equation for each turn.

Player A	Player B	Player C

Total leftovers: _____   Total leftovers: _____   Total leftovers: _____

Home Note: Your child records the equations from a division game played by three players.

Math Vocabulary

➤ Write new words and terms in the box.

➤ Write a definition, show an example, or draw a picture for each word or term in your list.

Home Note: Your child records terms and examples of math vocabulary.

Math Vocabulary

➤ Write new words and terms in the box.

➤ Write a definition, show an example, or draw a picture for each word or term in your list.

Math Vocabulary

Home Note: Your child records terms and examples of math vocabulary.

Student Glossary

divide

When we separate things into equal groups we use the word *divide*. For example, to share 12 cookies equally between 2 people we divide 12 into 2 equal groups so that each person gets 6 cookies.

divided by

We read 12 ÷ 4 = 3 this way: *12 divided by 4 is equal to 3*. The symbol ÷ means *divided by*.

division

Division is the word for what we do when we divide.

divisor

In a division equation such as 12 ÷ 3 = 4, 3 is the *divisor*. The *divisor* 3 tells us that there are 3 groups of 4 in 12.

equal groups

Equal groups means each group has the same amount. For example, if there are three circles and each circle has 2 stars, then there are three *equal groups* of two stars.

equation

An *equation* is a number sentence that uses an equal sign to show that two amounts have the same value. For example: 12 ÷ 3 = 4 is an equation.

grouping problem

A problem is a *grouping problem* when there are a number of things being put in equal groups.

An example of a *grouping problem* is:

There are 12 flowers.
(number to begin with)

You want to put 3 in each vase.
(equal groups)

How many vases of flowers would you have?
(number of groups)

We write it this way: 12 ÷ 3 = _____.
You would have 4 vases of flowers each with 3 flowers.

multiplication

When you write 2 × 3 = _____, you are asking, *What is the total for two groups of 3 (or 3 + 3).* We show *multiplication* with a times symbol (×).

Multiplication is another way of saying, *How many in all when there are a number of equal groups?*

quotient

The *quotient* is the answer to the question, How many equal groups of _____ are in _____? For example, *How many groups of 2 are in 25 or What is 25 divided by 2?* The answer is 12. There are 12 groups of 2 in 25 so 12 is the *quotient*.

Student Glossary

remainder

When we divide a number by another number we are finding the number of equal groups. Sometimes there are leftovers because there aren't enough to make another group.

For example, 8 ÷ 3 means *How many equal groups of 3 are in 8?*

Dividing 8 into groups of 3 gives us 2 groups of 3 with 2 left over. The 2 is the *remainder*.

We write it this way: 8 ÷ 3 = 2 R2

sharing problem

A problem is a *sharing problem* when there are a number of things being shared equally and you want to find out how many will be in each group.

An example of a *sharing problem* is:

> *There are 12 marbles.*
> (number to begin with)

> *3 friends are going to share them.*
> (number who will share)

> *How many marbles will each one get?*
> (how many in each group)

We write it this way: 12 ÷ 3 = _____.
Each friend will get 4 marbles.

symbols

You use *symbols* in mathematics to name numbers (12, 308, $\frac{1}{2}$), operations (+, −, ×, ÷), and relationships between numbers (=, >, <).

symbols for division

÷ means *is divided by*

$\frac{12}{3}$ The fraction bar is a division symbol. This means 12 divided by 3.

$3\overline{)12}$ The partial box around the 12 tells us that 12 is to be divided by 3. The quotient is written on the line above the 12.

$$3\overline{)12}^{\,4}$$

$$\text{divisor}\overline{)\text{dividend}}^{\,\text{quotient}}$$